Fast Facts About

DRAGONFLIES

by Julia Garstecki

Fast Facts About Insects & Spiders

Raintree is an imprint of Capstone Global Library Limited, a company incorporated in England and Wales having its registered office at 264 Banbury Road, Oxford, OX2 7DY – Registered company number: 6695582

www.raintree.co.uk
myorders@raintree.co.uk

Edited by Abby Huff
Designed by Kyle Grenz
Original illustrations © Capstone Global Library Limited
Picture research by Jo Miller
Production by Tori Abraham
Originated by Capstone Global Library Ltd

978 1 3982 1330 2 (hardback)
978 1 3982 1329 6 (paperback)

British Library Cataloguing in Publication Data
A full catalogue record for this book is available from the

Acknowledgements
We would like to thank the following for permission to reproduce photographs: Dreamstime: Evgeniya Murashova, 21; Newscom: imageBROKER/Dirk Funhoff, 17, Photoshot/NHPA/Stephen Dalton, 15; Shutterstock: Aliaksei Hintau, cover, Anan Suphap, 13, Andi111, 18, biker11, 6, Ger Bosma Photos, 9, Lane V. Erickson, 5, Martin Pelanek, 4, Mega Pixel, 20 (top right), Pheobus, 19, riphoto3, 20 (bottom right), SEDmi, 20 (top left), Sheva, 8, SweetLemons, 20 (middle right), timquo, 20 (bottom left), trgrowth, 11, Wayne Wolfersberger, 7, zabavina (background), cover and throughout

Every effort has been made to contact copyright holders of material reproduced in this book. Any omissions will be rectified in subsequent printings if notice is given to the publisher.

All the internet addresses (URLs) given in this book were valid at the time of going to press. However, due to the dynamic nature of the internet, some addresses may have changed, or sites may have changed or ceased to exist since publication. While the author and publisher regret any inconvenience this may cause readers, no responsibility for any such changes can be accepted by either the author or the publisher.

WEST NORTHAMPTONSHIRE COUNCIL	
60000508744	
Askews & Holts	
BH	

Printed and bound in India.

Contents

Words in **bold** are in the glossary.

All about dragonflies

Dragonflies are **insects**. A dragonfly has a long body. It has long wings. Dragonflies come in many colours. There are more than 2,500 types of dragonfly.

You can find dragonflies near ponds, lakes and streams. They live around the world. But they don't live in places where it is very cold all year long.

A dragonfly's body has three sections. On its head are two short **antennae**. It also has two large eyes. The eyes see in almost every direction.

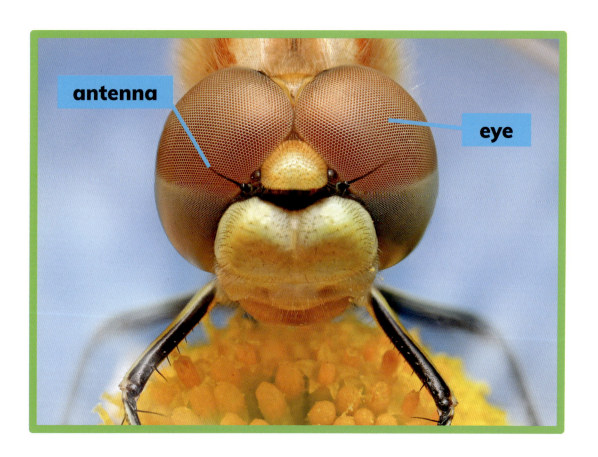

antenna

eye

wings

legs

The middle part of a dragonfly has six legs. It has four wings. The last body part is long and thin. It can curl up and down.

Dragonflies are fast. They fly faster than any other insect. They can flap all four wings at once. This helps them speed through the air.

Dragonflies can also move each wing on its own. This lets them fly backwards. They can also move to the sides. They can even fly steady in one place.

A dragonfly's life

A female dragonfly lays eggs in the water. A **nymph** hatches from each egg. The nymph is a dull colour. It has no wings. It lives in the water. It eats and grows.

Finally, the nymph has grown enough. It climbs out of the water. It sheds its skin. This is called **moulting**. Now it is a dragonfly!

Dragonfly life cycle

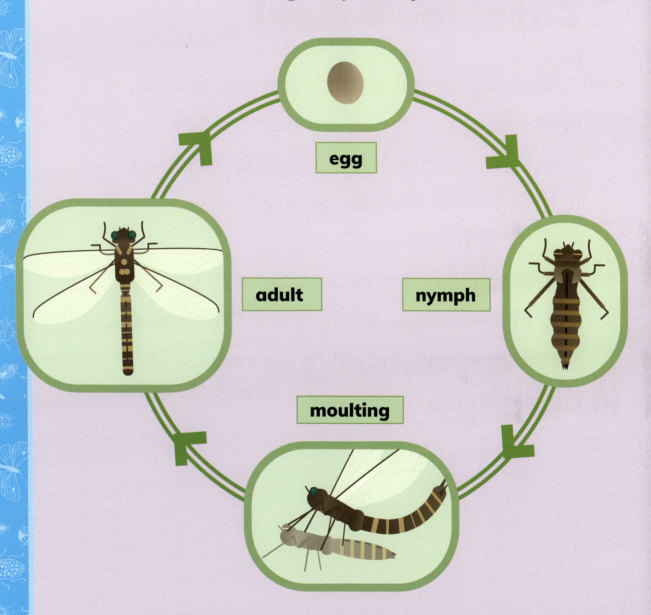

egg

nymph

moulting

adult

Catching a meal

Dragonflies are great **predators**. Some wait and watch for other insects. They chase any that fly by. Other dragonflies hunt in the air. They fly all day.

A dragonfly uses its legs to catch **prey**. Its legs make a shape like a basket. They scoop up prey. Dragonflies eat flying insects. That includes mosquitoes, bees and flies.

Nymphs are good hunters too. They hunt in the water. They feed on small insects and tiny fish.

A nymph has a special bottom lip. The lip shoots out. It has spikes on the end. These catch prey. The nymph pulls back its lip. It eats its prey.

A dragonfly nymph catches a fish.

Swarms

Dragonflies live alone most of the time. But sometimes many come together. This large group is called a **swarm**. A swarm may have millions of dragonflies.

Swarms happen when a lot of prey is in one place. The dragonflies hunt together. Swarms also happen in a fire or storm. Insects fly away. Dragonflies chase them.

Fun facts

- A dragonfly can reach speeds of up to 61 kilometres (38 miles) per hour.

- Dragonflies need to be warm in order to fly. Some sit in the sun. Others shake their wings to warm up.

- The first dragonflies lived more than 300 million years ago. Their wingspan was more than 0.6 metres (2 feet) long!

- Dragonflies can eat their own weight in 30 minutes. They even eat other dragonflies.

Make a dragonfly

What you need:

- craft stick
- wool or felt-tips
- two pipe cleaners
- glue
- two googly eyes

What to do:

1. Decorate the craft stick by wrapping it in wool or colouring it with felt-tips.

2. Bend both ends of one pipe cleaner to the middle. It should look like an eight. Repeat with the other pipe cleaner.

3. Glue the pipe cleaners to the craft stick to make wings. Glue the googly eyes to the other side of the stick.

Glossary

antenna feeler on an insect's head used to touch and smell

insect small animal with a hard outer shell, six legs, three body sections and two antennae

moult shed an outer layer of skin; after moulting, a new covering grows

nymph young form of an insect; nymphs grow into adults by moulting many times

predator animal that hunts other animals for food

prey animal hunted by another animal for food

swarm large group of insects gathered or flying together

Find out more

Books

Insects (Naturetrail), Rachel Firth (Usborne, 2014)

Insects and Spiders: Explore Nature with Fun Facts and Activities (Nature Explorers), DK (DK Children, 2019)

Life Cycles (Life Science Stories), Angela Royston (Raintree, 2017)

Websites

www.bbc.co.uk/earth/story/20160102-dragonflies-see-the-world-in-slow-motion
Watch this video to get a sense of how dragonflies see the world!

www.dkfindout.com/uk/animals-and-nature/insects/dragonflies-and-damselflies
Find out more about dragonflies and damselflies.

Index